For Lyd...
With than...

DRAW WITH ROB

HarperCollins Children's Books

First published in paperback in Great Britain by
HarperCollins *Children's Books* in 2020

HarperCollins *Children's Books* is a division of HarperCollins *Publishers* Ltd.
Text and illustrations copyright © Rob Biddulph 2020
The author/illustrator asserts the moral right to
be identified as the author/illustrator of the work.
A CIP catalogue record for this book is available from
the British Library. All rights reserved.

Visit our website at www.harpercollins.co.uk

135798642

ISBN: 978-0-00-841912-7
Printed and bound in the UK by
Bell & Bain Ltd.

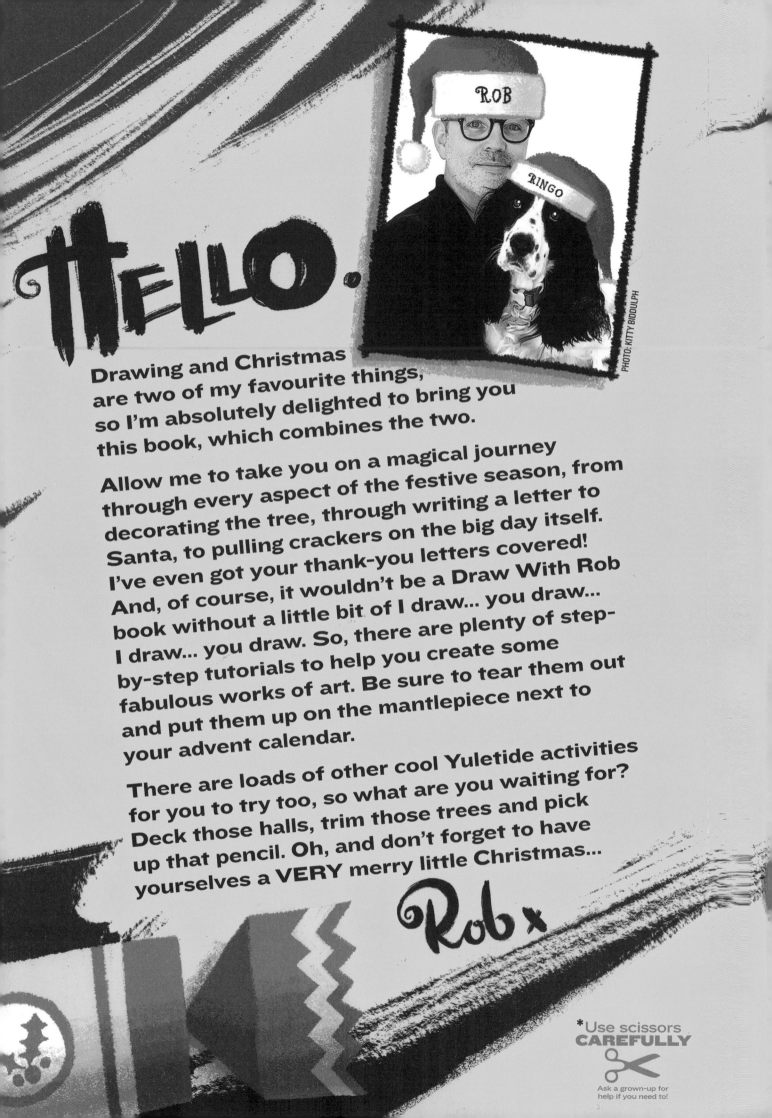

HELLO.

Drawing and Christmas are two of my favourite things, so I'm absolutely delighted to bring you this book, which combines the two.

Allow me to take you on a magical journey through every aspect of the festive season, from decorating the tree, through writing a letter to Santa, to pulling crackers on the big day itself. I've even got your thank-you letters covered! And, of course, it wouldn't be a Draw With Rob book without a little bit of I draw... you draw... you draw. So, there are plenty of step-by-step tutorials to help you create some fabulous works of art. Be sure to tear them out and put them up on the mantlepiece next to your advent calendar.

There are loads of other cool Yuletide activities for you to try too, so what are you waiting for? Deck those halls, trim those trees and pick up that pencil. Oh, and don't forget to have yourselves a VERY merry little Christmas...

Rob x

PHOTO: KITTY BIDDULPH

*Use scissors
CAREFULLY

Ask a grown-up for
help if you need to!

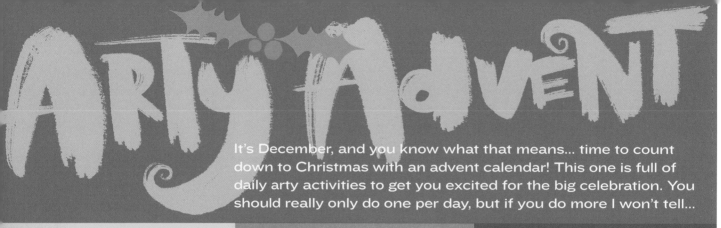

Arty Advent

It's December, and you know what that means... time to count down to Christmas with an advent calendar! This one is full of daily arty activities to get you excited for the big celebration. You should really only do one per day, but if you do more I won't tell...

1

Colour in Penguin Blue's present.

2

What's Lily pulling along on her sledge?

3

Ice the gingerbread man.

4

Decorate Monkey's balloon.

5

Finish off the reindeer's baubles.

6

SANTA'S LITTLE HELPER

Colour in Baboon's elf costume.

7

What's going on top of the tree?

8

Colour in the holly.

9

72

What Christmas song is Nancy singing?

10

TEDDY

Give Teddy a festive collar.

11

Colour in Kevin's bobble hat.

12

What giftwrap did Greg use?

13

What colour are the new underpants that Leonard's mum has bought him?

14

Colour in Oliver's Christmas onesie.

15

Give the Odd Dog Out a festive scarf and hat.

16

Light the Christmas candle.

17

What's on the astronaut's flag?

18
What's Fred having for Christmas dinner?

19

What colour hat does Wilbur have?

20

Make Martin's egg Christmassy.

21

What Christmas story is Eddie reading?

24

Design your own cracker.

22

Decorate the Yule log.

23

Colour in the elf's outfit.

WRITE on TIME

Before Father Christmas can deliver your presents he needs to know what you'd like, and the best way to tell him is by letter. Fill in the template (right) and then put it in an envelope with the label (below) attached. Penguin Blue, Boris and Zorg have already done theirs, so you'd better get started...

Dear FATHER CHRISTMAS

This year I have mainly been
naughty ☐ nice ☑ a little bit of both ☐

What I would really like for Christmas is

Some fish

and

some more fish

I promise that I will leave you and your reindeer

a fish

on Christmas Eve.

Merry Christmas! Love from

Penguin Blue X

Dear FATHER CHRISTMAS

This year I have mainly been
naughty ☐ nice ☐ a little bit of both ☒

What I would really like for Christmas is

A gold medal

and

a hug

... I will leave you and your reindeer

mince pie & a carrot

... Christmas Eve.

... Christmas! Love from

Boris Bear

Dear FATHER CHRISTMAS

This year I have mainly been
naughty ☐ nice ☑ a little bit of both ☐

I would really like for Christmas is

... will leave you and your reindeer

... Christmas Eve.

... Christmas! Love from

Zorg

To FATHER CHRISTMAS

Santa's Grotto
Reindeerland
XM4 5HQ

Please cut out **CAREFULLY**

Ask a grown-up for help!

Dear grown-up, this is Santa's official address!

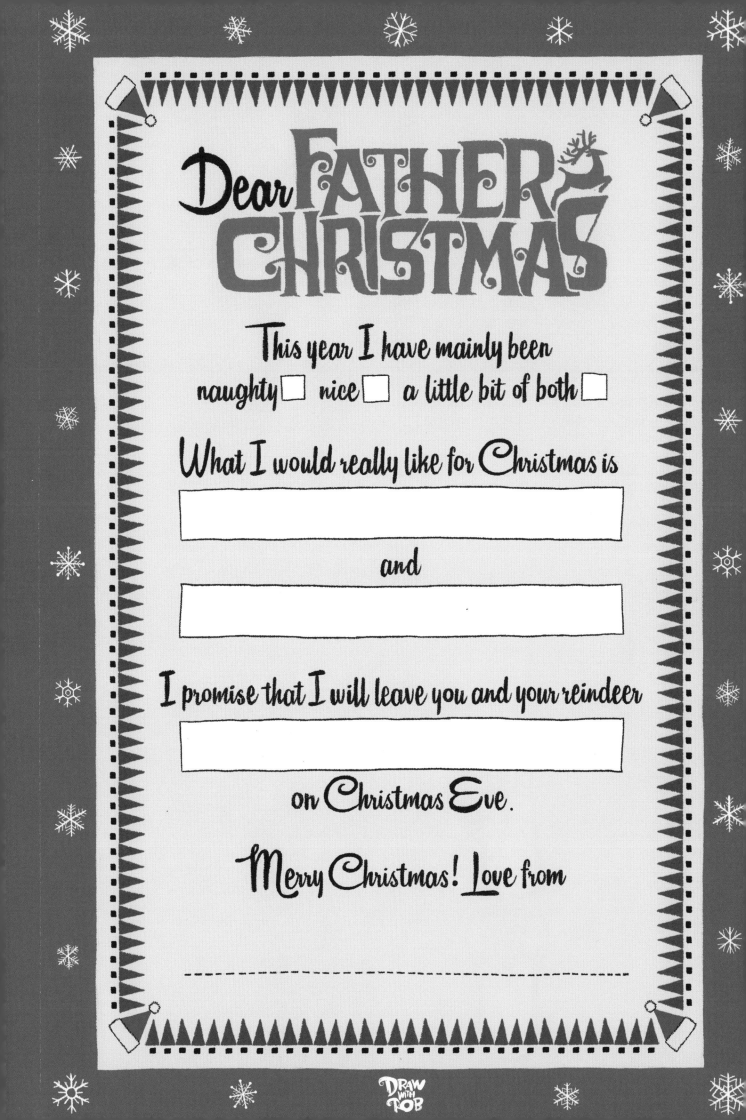

Dear FATHER CHRISTMAS

This year I have mainly been
naughty ☐ nice ☐ a little bit of both ☐

What I would really like for Christmas is

and

I promise that I will leave you and your reindeer

on Christmas Eve.

Merry Christmas! Love from

ONE, TWO, TREE!

It's beginning to look a lot like Christmas, and the penguins and Fred are loving decorating their tree. Isn't it fabulous? Make your own tree beautiful by designing, colouring in and cutting out the decorations on the following pages. Then tie them to the branches using some string. One, two, tree... Penguin perfect!

Xmas decorations

Please cut out CAREFULLY

Ask a grown-up for help!

Please cut out
CAREFULLY

Ask a grown-up for help!

Please cut out
CAREFULLY

Ask a grown-up for help!

Please cut out
CAREFULLY
Ask a grown-up for help!

DRAW WITH ROB

Meet Clive the POLAR BEAR

Clive is ready to celebrate Christmas with his friends from **Blown Away!** He's all wrapped up in his jolly jumper, and ready to go shopping for the perfect present. Let's learn how to draw him and send him on his way!

Joyeux NOËL

How to DRAW...
Clive

From the books *Blown Away* and *Sunk!*

1 Let's start at the top of the page with a small sideways oval, slightly pointy at the bottom. Add some smaller semicircles at each end for his ears, like you see here.

2 Give Clive a nose. Draw a rectangle down from the top of his head as shown and colour in the bottom third.

3 Draw two dots on either side. These are his eyes. Add a small line above each of them to give him eyebrows, and a small circle inside each ear.

4 Draw a sideways rectangle with curved corners just below his head, like you see here.

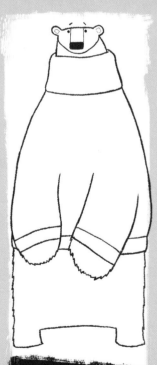

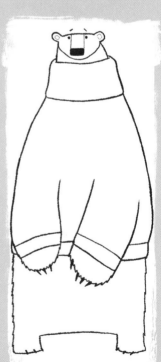

5 Time to give Clive a jumper. Draw two diagonal lines coming down from his neck as shown. Then curve them into arm shapes. Make his paws shaggy at the bottom.

6 Add two lines on the bottom of each arm for jumper cuffs. One on the bottom too. Then draw a shaggy square shape for his body, with a rectangle on each side for legs.

7 As we all know, a polar bear needs claws. Draw them in here, on each paw. And don't forget the ones on his feet!

8 It's time to give Clive some colour! Add some scribbly shadow under each paw and make his jumper as **Christmassy** as you can, using any colours you like.

CLIVE

By.. **Age**...........

A Better SWEATER

The **Dinosaur Juniors** are getting wrapped up and ready for Christmas too! Design and colour in their festive pullovers, and remember: the jollier the jumper, the better the sweater!

Wilf

Otto

Winnie

Season's greetings

Share the love and spread the season's joy by swapping some **Christmas cards** with your family and friends this year! There are two cards here to tear out and add your own art to, but why not make more? The only limit is your imagination...

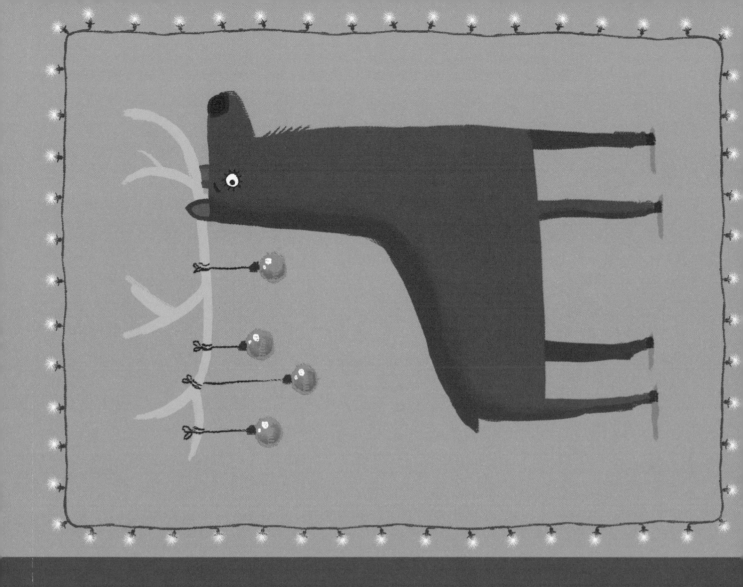

By *Rob Biddulph* and

A picture. By me.

MERRY CHRISTMAS

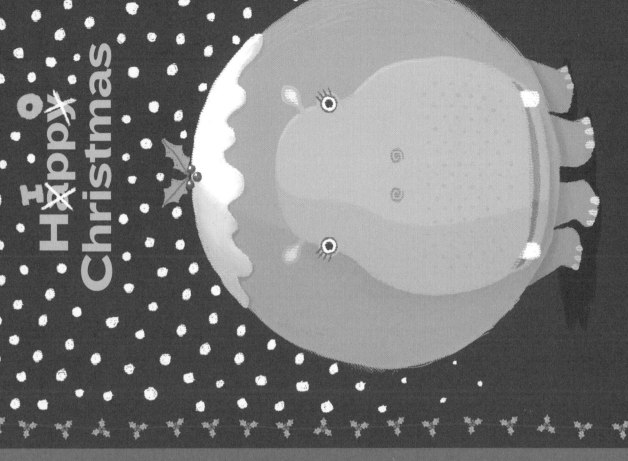

Happy Christmas

Draw with Rob

By Rob Biddulph and

A picture. By me.

Colour Me CHRISTMAS

Dave and Teddy from the book **Dog Gone** are having fun in the cold. Snow might be white in the real world, but there's no need for this page to be boring. Use your best colours to brighten it up and bring them some Christmas cheer, then find out how to draw your own snowman, just over the page!

a snowman

1 Start at the top of the page by drawing a simple hat shape at a slight angle.

2 Under that, draw a circle for his head. Easy.

3 Okay, let's give our snowman a face. A carrot shape in the middle of his head for a nose, two dots above it for eyes and a curved dotty line below for a nice wide smile.

4 Next, add a small rectangular shape with curved corners underneath his head.

5 Then draw another circle below that for the top part of his body. Draw a curved rectangle shape to the right as shown, and add some fringing to finish his scarf.

6 Draw a slightly bigger circle to finish the snowman's body.

7 Add three dots under his scarf for buttons, and some thick, angular lines for his stick arms. Some more smaller lines at the end of those will give him fingers.

8 Your snowman is ready for some colour. Add some shadows too. Just because I have kept my colours traditional doesn't mean you have to. Go crazy!

SNOWMAN

By.. **Age**...............

WORDLY WONDERLAND

Kevin and Sid are searching for the Christmassy words hidden in this grid. Can you help? Don't forget to tick them off the list as you find them...

Words can run forwards, backwards, diagonally and even upside down!

COMPILED BY POPPY BIDDULPH

T	L	G	F	Y	S	L	E	I	G	H	V	I	M	L
U	A	N	U	R	P	I	X	T	Q	W	O	P	I	F
R	B	I	R	Z	R	E	I	N	D	E	E	R	S	L
K	E	K	T	I	H	U	C	S	T	O	D	E	T	E
E	C	C	P	S	B	H	O	L	L	Y	I	S	L	U
Y	P	O	L	P	A	B	F	E	G	O	M	E	E	R
G	A	T	C	N	Z	N	Y	R	V	U	S	N	T	W
R	A	S	L	P	E	C	T	B	Q	A	I	T	O	R
A	Z	H	O	M	E	E	R	A	N	O	S	N	E	I
T	A	O	D	L	A	E	T	T	S	C	S	M	D	B
S	T	L	B	E	J	G	R	K	E	K	I	X	A	B
J	N	U	F	M	I	N	C	E	P	I	E	K	G	O
U	A	D	L	H	I	C	E	G	P	N	P	O	P	N
B	P	L	B	A	U	B	L	Y	A	G	R	F	T	E
A	D	P	A	I	D	C	L	E	S	N	I	T		

Words to find

- [ ] BAUBLE
- [ ] ELF
- [ ] HOLLY
- [ ] MINCE PIE
- [ ] MISTLETOE
- [ ] PRESENT
- [ ] REINDEER
- [ ] RIBBON
- [ ] SANTA
- [ ] SLEIGH
- [ ] SNOW
- [ ] STAR
- [ ] STOCKING
- [ ] TINSEL
- [ ] TURKEY

The PERFECT PAPER

It's time to swap presents, but first I need you to design the perfect paper. Go Christmas crazy with lots of colours and patterns, then wrap this thing up by adding names to the labels!

to Holly

To Darcy

to Quinn

Turn the page to **unwrap** the gifts

10 the PERFECT PRESENT

Now that the paper is perfect, it's time to look at the presents themselves. Open up your imagination and draw what you think is inside the wrapping paper. What about making one of them your perfect present?

To Darcy

to Holly

KEITH

REALLY REALLY FAST

72

RAPID

CHOP CHOP

PRONTO

BRISK

RAPID

72

ZOOM

ZOOM

to Quinn

Turn back a page to **wrap** the gifts

Spot the Difference

The festive forest gift hunt

Fred Bear and his pals are looking for presents in the fir tree forest. See if you can spot the **six** differences between these two scenes and write what they are in the spaces below.

1 ....

2 ....

3 ....

4 ....

5 ....

6 ....

Boxing Clever

Presents don't have to be big to be special – something small in a beautiful box can be the best gift of all. Read the instructions below and use the template opposite to create your own little box of Christmas magic, and use it to give someone special the perfect present.

INSTRUCTIONS

1 Cut out the template opposite and fold all the dotted lines in towards the base, as shown. The dotted lines go on the inside of the box.

2 Use your glue to stick down the tabs 1–4 where shown. This will keep your box together. Leave the tabs around the top and on the lid free so that you can put your present inside and close it up.

3 When the glue is dry, you're ready to wrap! If your present might rattle around, you can use coloured paper or cotton wool to make it extra special and to give it something soft to rest on.

4 For the final touch, tie a Christmas ribbon around your beautiful box with a nice big bow on top.

MERRY CHRISTMAS – LET'S GET GIFTING!

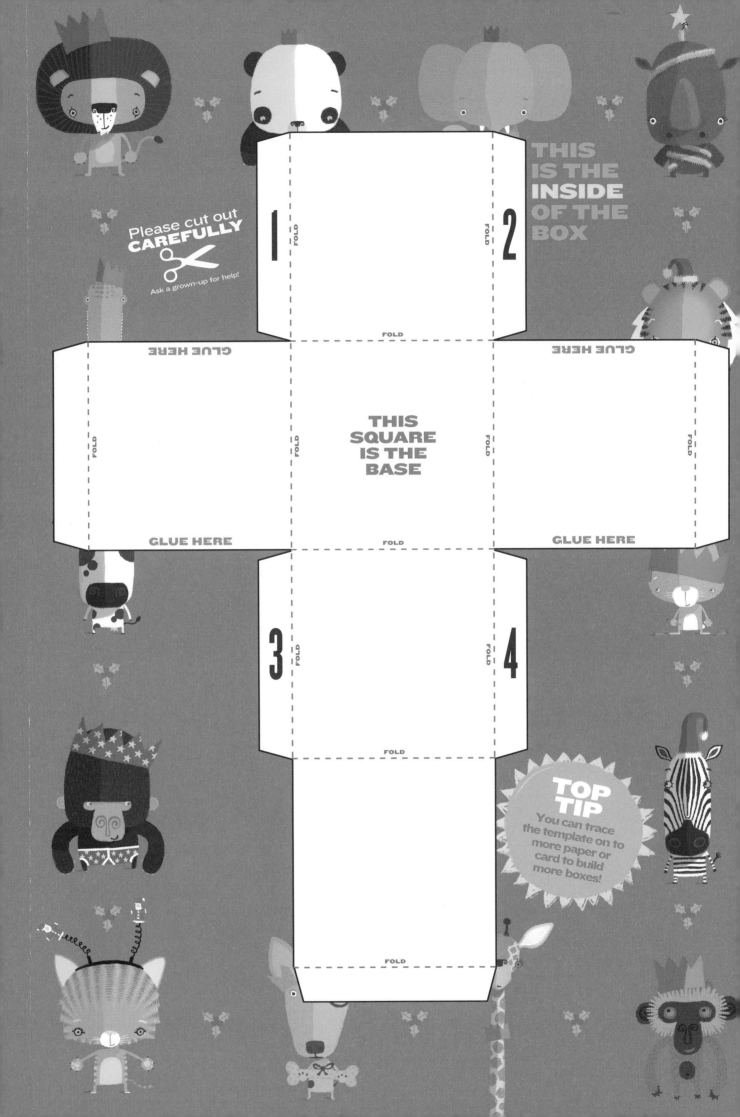

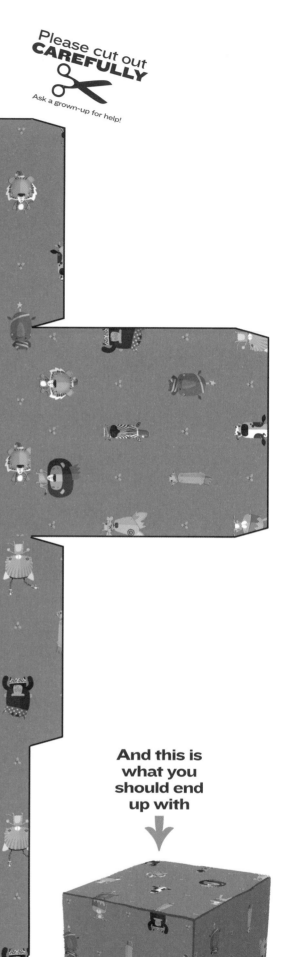

THIS
IS THE
OUTSIDE
OF THE
BOX

Please cut out
CAREFULLY
Ask a grown-up for help!

And this is
what you
should end
up with

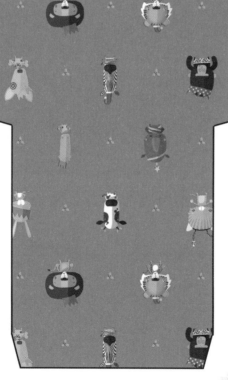

Meet the Elves

Christmas just wouldn't
be possible without
Santa's Little Helpers
– the elves! Turn the page and
let's learn how to draw one.

an elf portrait

1 **Start your elf with a crown!**
Draw a straight horizontal line,
then add a series of spikes along
the top, like you see here.

2 **Next, draw a circle above and
to the left with a rectangle across
the middle and a dot at the bottom.
That's the bell! Join it to the crown
with two curved lines as shown.**

3 **Draw some more spikes,
but this time they should be
pointing downwards. That's
your elf's hair. Then add
a square for their head.**

4 **Now give your elf a face. Add
two circles with dots for eyes, and
some curved lines for the mouth
and nose, as shown. Don't forget
to add eyelashes and eyebrows.**

5 **Ears next! Draw a big triangle
with a curved bottom on either
side of the head. Add a swirl
in the middle as shown. Sketch
another upside-down crown shape
underneath the face.**

6 **Your elf's belt is made
up of a long rectangle interrupted
by two rounded rectangles in
the middle, Join it to the collar
with two vertical lines and
add some buttons.**

7 **Draw two bent tube shapes,
one on either side of the body.
These, believe it or not, are your
elf's arms. Add some circles at the
bottom for hands and some
zigzags for cuffs.**

8 **Add a curved U-shape under the
belt and two rectangles for legs.
Draw two more rectangles with curly
tips, as shown, for shoes. Then finish
with some spikes near the ankles,
just like you did for the cuffs.**

9 **Now your elf just needs
some brightening up! Use all
your elvish tricks to add some
Christmassy colours. Oh, and don't
forget the scribbly shadow.**

By.. Age............

My Elf Portrait

ODD DOG IN

It might be cold outside, but it's nice and warm indoors at the **Odd Dog Out** fancy-dress Christmas party! Join the sausage dogs and make their celebration wild and wonderful by colouring it in.

HOT DOG

Get Ready to

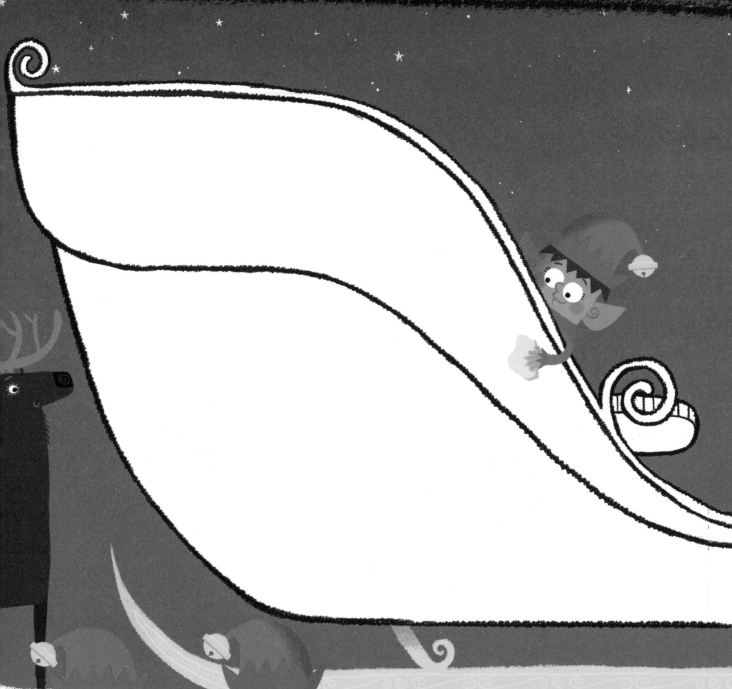

SLEIGH!

The big day is almost here, and the elves are polishing up the sleigh for Santa. Design the most spectacular ride you can and then colour it in so that Father Christmas can deliver his presents in style when he's finally ready to roll...

How to DRAW...
a reindeer

1 Let's start at the top. Draw a small spike in the middle of the page. Not too pointy, though!

2 From the bottom left of the spike, draw a horizontal line, then curve it down and around as shown here.

3 Add an eye by drawing a circle with a dot in it, with some lines for eyelashes. A swirl will do for a nose and a small curve for a smile. Put a triangle inside the ear too, as shown.

4 For your reindeer's back, draw straight down from the ear and then head off to the right in a gentle curve. Then nip that in a tiny bit to start the tail.

5 Next, draw a line down from the snout. Make it zigzagged at the top like you see here. Keep going down the page until you're below the tail, and then turn sharp right.

6 Let's finish the outline. Draw two long, thin rectangles for legs, and join them up in the middle with a straight line. Add two black hooves at the bottom.

7 Add your reindeer's other legs – two more rectangles as shown. Again, colour the tips in black for the hooves.

8 Draw in the antlers by adding long, thin sausage shapes at the top like you see here. Join them to your reindeer's head just in front of the ear. Make sure you have lots of sticky-uppy bits!

9 Now colour in your reindeer. You'll need to add shadows under the hooves too. Use as many colours as you like. Go wild!

What's in SANTA'S SACK?

The gifts have been wrapped, the reindeer are ready to go, and **Santa's Little Helpers** have made sure his sack is perfectly packed! Use your drawing skills to fill it with toys, presents and any other festive delights that you can think of.

Etic

FLYING HOME for CHRISTMAS

Zorg the Explorer spends the whole year travelling around the universe, but at Christmas he always heads back to Alpha Centauri to spend time with his family. Can you get him back to his spaceship so he can fly home for the festivities?

Meet

FATHER CHRISTMAS

He's making a list... He's checking it twice...
That's right, **Santa Claus** is nearly ready to
come to town. Happily, he's always pleased
to say hello or give you a very jolly ho, ho, ho!
Let's leave him to his final preparations while
we turn the page and learn how to draw him...

Father Christmas

1 Let's start by drawing two simple shapes next to each other at the top of our page: a circle and a rectangle

2 Next, add two curvy lines joining them up, as shown. This is Santa's hat!

3 Now add two large teardrop shapes that mirror each other and kiss in the middle (his moustache) and two small rectangles (his eyebrows).

4 Draw a small semicircle and a line for his nose, two small dots for smiley eyes, two circles and a line for glasses and two curved lines for the sides of his head.

5 Time for my favourite bit: his beard! Make yours as bouncy and fluffy as mine by drawing an upside down cloud shape between the two corners of his hat.

6 Next, add three more rectangles as shown (one long, two short).

7 Some more detail now. Draw arms and mittens as shown, then add two vertical lines that join the long rectangle to his beard. Add a small circle on his tummy.

8 Finally, add his legs and boots as shown.

9 Time to colour! I've stuck to the traditional red and white, but did you know that Father Christmas was originally said to wear green?

FATHER CHRISTMAS

By .... Age ....

SLEEP...

Dinosaur Juniors Winnie and Otto are fast asleep and dreaming of morning, when they'll wake up to a Christmas Day full of family fun, fabulous festivities and fantastic food! Why don't you draw what you think they're dreaming of...

Much Ado About Stuffing

It's time to eat! Mr Lumsden, the kindly teacher from the book **Show and Tell**, has cooked a delicious Christmas dinner for Class 2L to enjoy, but what has he served up? Why don't you add your favourite food to the empty plates...

EDDIE

FLORENCE

GEORGE

VIOLET

ULYSSES

THEA

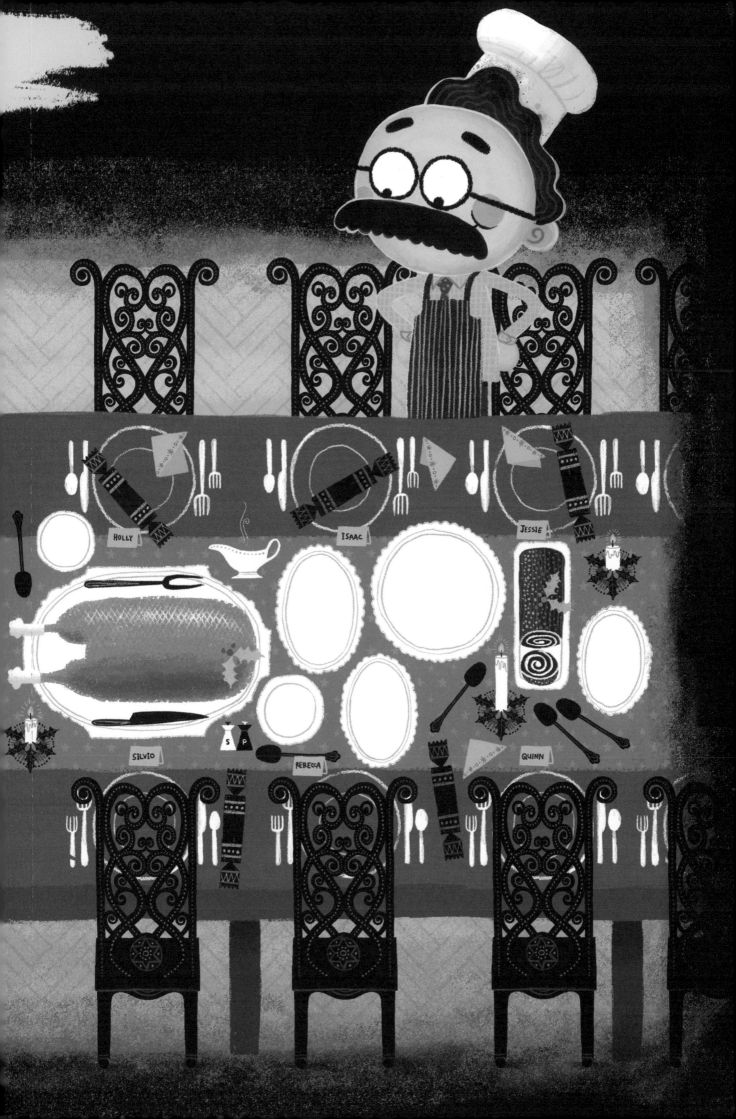

Christmas cRacK-UP!

JOKES COMPILED BY KITTY AND POPPY BIDDULPH

Dinner was a winner, but the fun isn't over yet... Let's pull some crackers and get giggling! Cracker jokes are always the best, so cut along the dotted lines on the page opposite and share the laughs at your dinner table. There are also some charades and (on the flip side) Guess the Sketch suggestions for after-dinner games. Don't forget to add your own ideas to the blank ones!

Please cut out CAREFULLY

Ask a grown-up for help!

Joke

What do snowmen wear
on their heads?
Ice caps

Charade

Elf (film)

Joke

What do Santa's little helpers
learn at school?
The Elf-abet

Charade

"Silent Night" (song)

Joke

What is a dog's favourite
Christmas carol?
"Bark, the Herald Angels Sing"

Charade

A Christmas Carol (book)

Joke

Why are Christmas trees
bad at knitting?
**Because they are always
dropping their needles**

Charade

Frozen (film)

Joke

Who hides in the bakery
at Christmas?
A mince spy

Charade

**"Fairytale of
New York"** (song)

Joke

Why was the snowman
looking at the carrots?
Because he was picking his nose

Charade

***How the Grinch
Stole Christmas!*** (book)

Joke

Why is it getting harder to
buy advent calendars?
Because their days are numbered

Charade

Nativity! (film)

Joke

What do you get if you eat
Christmas decorations?
Tinsel-itus

Charade

**"The Little
Drummer Boy"** (song)

Joke

How does Darth Vader like
his Christmas turkey?
On the dark side

Charade

***Father Christmas
Needs a Wee!*** (book)

Joke

What do you call
a penguin in a desert?
Lost

Charade

***The Nightmare
Before Christmas*** (film)

Joke

What do snowmen eat
for breakfast?
Ice Krispies

Charade

"We Three Kings" (song)

Joke

What do they use when there
are roadworks in the North Pole?
Snow cones

Charade

Mog's Christmas (book)

Joke

What does Santa suffer from
if he gets stuck in a chimney?
Claus-trophobia

Charade

It's a Wonderful Life (film)

Joke

What do fish sing at Christmas?
Christmas corals

Charade

**"Let it Snow! Let it Snow!
Let it Snow!"** (song)

Joke

Charade

Joke

Charade

Joke

Charade

Joke

Charade

Father Christmas

A Christmas tree

A Christmas cracker

A reindeer

An elf

A Christmas present

A Christmas stocking

A snowman

A turkey

A robin

A bauble

A Christmas pudding

Some holly

Santa's sleigh

TESTIVE FUNNIES

Class 2L are cracking up, but what are they laughing at? Add your funniest joke in the space provided, and then give their laughter some colour!

My favourite joke ever

THANK YOU!

**Thankyou
verymuch**

Thank you

MERCI

BEAUCOUP

Dear

....

Thank you for

....

....

....

....

....

Love from

....

DRAW WITH ROB

Dear

....

Thank you for

....

....

....

....

....

Love from

....

DRAW WITH ROB

Dear

....

Thank you for

....

....

....

....

....

Love from

....

DRAW WITH ROB

Dear

....

Thank you for

....

....

....

....

....

Love from

....

DRAW WITH ROB

LOVE MY GIFT

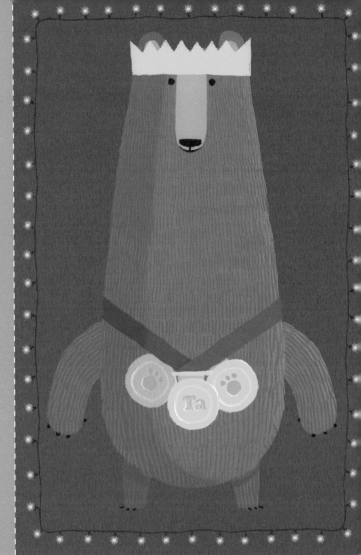

Thanks

Thank you

Dear

Thank you for

Love from

DRAW WITH ROB

Dear

Thank you for

Love from

DRAW WITH ROB

Dear

Thank you for

Love from

DRAW WITH ROB

Dear

Thank you for

Love from

DRAW WITH ROB

GOODBYE!

Congratulations on reaching the end of the book! I really hope you've enjoyed our festive adventures together. But just because the season is over, the fun doesn't have to be. You can enjoy my characters all year round by reading about them in my books. Merry Christmas!

And don't forget to watch all of my **#DrawWithRob** videos on my YouTube channel and follow me on social media

@RobBiddulph @rbiddulph RobBiddulphAuthor Rob Biddulph @RobBiddulph

www.robbiddulph.com

ANSWERS

WORDY WONDERLAND

THE FESTIVE FOREST GIFT HUNT

THE LAPLAND GANG

FLYING HOME FOR CHRISTMAS